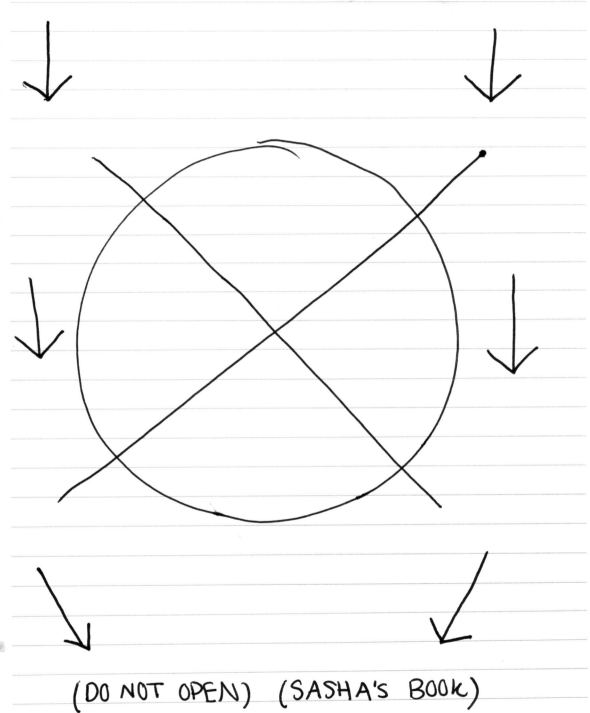

(DO NOT OPEN) (SASHA'S BOOK)

"Your life will reflect what you expect"

we leave for camp in a couple days so already everyone is pretty stressed. we went to TJmax today, ortho, and went to see pop at the beach. when we got home I realized I left my phone at the beach. I am so upset bcause it had all my pictures, contacts, and music on it for camp. I really hope I can find it
        xoxo Sasha (June 20 2017)

Your life
will Reflect

your life will reflect YOUR LIFE WILL REFLECT
WHAT YOU EXPECT

"Don't stumble over something behind you"

Blessed are the curious for they shall have Adventures

If you are
sad you are living
in the Past.
If you are anxious
you are living in the
future.
If you are at Peace
you are living
in the Now.

There
are only two
mistakes one can
make along
the way:

Not going all the way
and
not starting.

BUDDHA

God grant me the Serenity to accept the things I cannot change, Courage to change the things I can, and wisdom to know the difference.

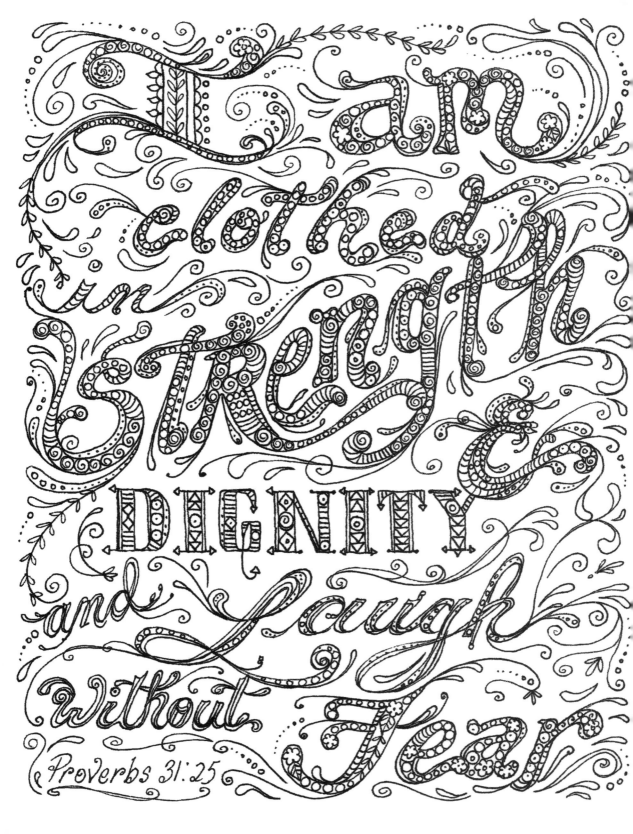

I am clothed in Strength & DIGNITY and Laugh without Fear

Proverbs 31:25

Let yourself
be open
and life will be
EASIER.

Be Happy Positive Grateful Patient Loving Forgiving Kind Real

No one can do it for you, choose to use your wings

EVERY
* DAY *
is a
NEW
Beginning

LIFE

doesn't have to be
perfect
to
be

Wonderful

DO WHAT
is right,
NOT WHAT
is easy.

Andrews McMeel Publishing
a division of Andrews McMeel Universal
1130 Walnut Street, Kansas City, Missouri 64106

www.andrewsmcmeel.com

15 16 17 18 19 PAH 10 9 8 7 6 5 4 3 2 1

ISBN: 978-1-4494-7813-1

Attention: Schools and Businesses
Andrews McMeel books are available at quantity discounts with bulk purchase for
educational, business, or sales promotional use. For information, please e-mail the
Andrews McMeel Publishing Special Sales Department: specialsales@amuniversal.com.